If You Should Meet a Crocodile
and other poems

Compiled by Tig Thomas

Miles
KeLLY

First published in 2010 by Miles Kelly Publishing Ltd
Harding's Barn, Bardfield End Green, Thaxted, Essex, CM6 3PX, UK

2 4 6 8 10 9 7 5 3 1

Editorial Director Belinda Gallagher

Art Director Jo Cowan

Assistant Editor Claire Philip

Designer Joe Jones

Junior Designer Kayleigh Allen

Production Manager Elizabeth Collins

Reprographics Stephan Davis, Ian Paulyn

ISBN 978-1-84810-371-9

Printed in China

British Library Cataloguing-in-Publication Data
A catalogue record for this book is available from the British Library

ACKNOWLEDGEMENTS

The publishers would like to thank Kirsten Wilson for
the illustrations she contributed to this book.

All other artwork from the Miles Kelly Artwork Bank

The publishers would like to thank iStockphoto.com for the use
of their photographs on pages 24 (Stanislav Pobytov) and 28 (Ewa Mazur)

Made with paper from a sustainable forest

www.mileskelly.net
info@mileskelly.net

www.factsforprojects.com

Self-publish your
children's book

buddingpress.co.uk

Contents

Wouldn't it be Funny? 4
Anonymous

Amelia *A E Housman* 6

Why? *Anonymous* 7

Some Puzzles *Anonymous* 8

Brother and Sister 10
Lewis Carroll

Time *Christina Rossetti* 12

The Mermaid and the 14
Sailor Boy *A E Housman*

The Ferry of Shadowtown 16
Ethelbert Nevin

The Falling Star *Sara Teasdale* 18

White Sheep *Anonymous* 19

Caterpillar *Christina Rossetti* 20

Butterfly *Benjamin Franklin* 20

Hurt no Living Thing 21
Christina Rossetti

From **Strange Meetings** 22
Harold Monro

Baby Seed Song *E Nesbit* 23

All the Year Round 24
Sara Coleridge

Child's Song in Spring 26
E Nesbit

Daffy-Down-Dilly *Anonymous* 28

Spring, the Sweet Spring 29
Thomas Nashe

The Man with the Beard 30
Edward Lear

There was an Old Man 31
Edward Lear

If you Should Meet a 32
Crocodile *Anonymous*

The Little Cock-sparrow 33
Anonymous

The Man who went Mad 34
Anonymous

The Lady of Antigua 36
G K Chesterton

The Young Lady of Norway 37
Edward Lear

A Ride *Anonymous* 38

Index of First Lines 40

Mia-ow Mia-ow

Wouldn't it be Funny?

Wouldn't it be funny —
Wouldn't it, now —
If the dog said, "Moo-oo"
And the cow said, "Bow-wow"?
If the cat sang and whistled,
And the bird said, "Mia-ow"?
Wouldn't it be funny —
Wouldn't it, now?

Anonymous

Moo-oo

4

Mia-ow

BOW-WOW BOW-WOW Bow-wow

MOO-OO MOO-OO

Amelia

Amelia mixed the mustard,
She mixed it good and thick:
She put it in the custard
And made her Mother sick,
And showing satisfaction
By many loud huzza
"Observe" she said "the action
Of mustard on Mamma."

A E Housman

Why?

There was a young maid who said, "Why
Can't I look in my ear with my eye?
If I give my mind to it,
I'm sure I can do it,
You never can tell till you try."

Anonymous

Some Puzzles

The Man in the Wilderness asked of me

"How many blackberries grow in the sea?"

I answered him as I thought good.

"As many red herrings as grow in the wood."

The Man in the Wilderness asked me why
His hen could swim, and his pig could fly.
I answered him briskly as I thought best.
"Because they were born in a cuckoo's nest."

The Man in the Wilderness asked me to tell
The sands in the sea and I counted them well.
Says he with a grin **"And not one more?"**
I answered him bravely, **"You go and make sure."**

Anonymous

Brother and Sister

"Sister, sister, go to bed!
Go and rest your weary head."
Thus the prudent brother said.

"Do you want a battered hide,
Or scratches to your face applied?"
Thus his sister calm replied.

"Sister, do not raise my wrath.
    I'd make you into mutton broth
        As easily as kill a moth"

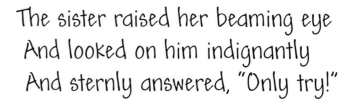

The sister raised her beaming eye
And looked on him indignantly
And sternly answered, "Only try!"

Off to the cook he quickly ran.
"Dear Cook, please lend a frying pan
To me as quickly as you can."

"And wherefore should I lend it you?"
"The reason, Cook, is plain to view.
I wish to make an Irish stew."

"What meat is in that stew to go?"
"My sister'll be the contents!"
    "Oh"
"You'll lend the pan to me, Cook?"
    "No!"

Moral: Never stew your sister.

Lewis Carroll

Time

How many seconds in a minute?
Sixty, and no more in it.

How many minutes in an hour?
Sixty, for sun and shower.

How many hours in a day?
Twenty-four, for work and play.

How many days in a week?
Seven, both to hear and speak.

How many weeks in a month?
Four, as the swift moon runn'th.

How many months in a year?
Twelve, the almanack makes clear.

How many years in an age?
One hundred, says the sage.

How many ages in time?
No one knows the rhyme.

Christina Rossetti

Almanack a
calendar containing
useful information

The Mermaid
and the Sailor Boy

There was a gallant sailor-boy who'd crossed the harbour bar
And sailed in many a foreign main – in fact he was a tar;
And leaning o'er the good ship's side into the deep looked he
When a skimpy little mermaid came swimming o'er the sea.
She was very scaly, and sang in every scale;
And then she cried "Encore! Encore!" and wagged her little tail
Till she came to the good ship's side, and saw the sailor-boy above
And a pang shot through her little heart, for she found she was in love.
She opened conversation, very cleverly, she thought.
"Have you spliced the capstan-jib, my boy? Is the tarpaulin taut?"
The sailor-boy was candid, he let his mirth appear –
He did not strive to hide his smile – he grinned from ear to ear.

She noticed his amusement, and it gave her feelings pain,
And her tail grew still more skimpy, as she began again.
"Oh, will you come and live with me? And you shall have delight
In catching limpets all the day and eating them all night;
And lobsters in abundance in the palace where I am;
And I will come and be thy bride, and make thee seaweed jam."
The sailor-boy did shut one eye, and then did it unclose;
And with solemnity he put his thumb unto his nose;
And said "Be bothered if I do, however much you sing;
You flabby little, dabby little, wetty little thing."

A E Housman

Tar sailor

The Ferry of Shadowtown

Sway to and fro in the twilight grey;
This is the ferry for Shadowtown;
It always sails at the end of
the day,
Just as the darkness
closes down.

Rest, little head, on my shoulder so
A sleepy kiss is the only fare;
Drifting away from the world we go,
Baby and I in the rocking chair.

See, where the fire logs glow and spark,
Glitter the lights of the shadowland;
The raining drops on the window, hark!
Are ripples lapping upon its strand.

There, where the mirror is glancing dim,
A lake lies shimmering, cool and still;
Blossoms are waving above its brim,
Those over there on the window sill.

Rock slow, more slow, in the dusky light,
Silently lower the anchor down,
Dear little passenger, say "Good night!"
We've reached the harbour for Shadowtown!

Ethelbert Nevin

The Falling Star

I saw a star slide down the sky,
Blind the north as it went by,
Too burning and too quick to hold,
Too lovely to be bought or sold,
Good only to make wishes on
And then forever to be gone.

Sara Teasdale

White Sheep

White sheep, white sheep,
On a blue hill,
When the wind stops
You all stand still.

When the wind blows,
You walk away slow.
White sheep, white sheep,
Where do you go?

Anonymous

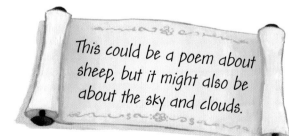

This could be a poem about sheep, but it might also be about the sky and clouds.

Caterpillar

Brown and furry
Caterpillar in a hurry,
Take your walk
To the shady leaf, or stalk,
Or what not,
Which may be the chosen spot.
No toad spy you,
Hovering bird of prey pass by you;
Spin and die,
To live again a butterfly.

Christina Rossetti

Butterfly

What is a butterfly? At best
He's but a caterpillar dressed.

Benjamin Franklin

Hurt no Living Thing

Hurt no living thing:
Ladybird, nor butterfly,
Nor moth with dusty wing,
Nor cricket chirping cheerily,
Nor grasshopper so light of leap,
Nor dancing gnat, nor beetle fat,
Nor harmless worms that creep.

Christina Rossetti

Tweet tweet! tweet tweet!

From *Strange Meetings*

The stars must make an awful noise
In whirling round the sky;
Yet somehow I can't even hear
Their loudest song or sigh.

So it is wonderful to think
One blackbird can outsing
The voice of all the swarming stars
On any day in Spring.

Harold Monro

Baby Seed Song

Little brown seed, oh! little brown brother,
Are you awake in the dark?
Here we lie cosily, close to each other:
Hark to the song of the lark —

    "Waken!" the lark says, "waken
      and dress you,
    Put on your green coats and gay,
    Blue sky will shine on you, sunshine
      caress you —
    Waken! 'tis morning — 'tis May!"

  Little brown brother, oh! little brown brother,
What kind of flower will you be?
I'll be a poppy — all white, like my mother;
 Do be a poppy like me.
  What! You're a sunflower? How I shall miss you
 When you're grown golden and high!
But I shall send all the bees up to kiss you;
Little brown brother, goodbye!

E Nesbit

All the Year Round

January brings the snow,
makes our feet and fingers glow.

February brings the rain,
Thaws the frozen lake again.

March brings breezes loud and shrill,
stirs the dancing daffodil.

April brings the primrose sweet,
Scatters daises at our feet.

May brings flocks of pretty lambs,
Skipping by their fleecy dams.

June brings tulips, lilies, roses,
Fills the children's hands with posies.

Hot **July** brings cooling showers,
Apricots and gillyflowers.

August brings the sheaves of corn,
Then the harvest home is borne.

Warm **September** brings the fruit,
Sportsmen then begin to shoot.

Fresh **October** brings the pheasants,
Then to gather nuts is pleasant.

Dull **November** brings the blast,
Then the leaves are whirling fast.

Chill **December** brings the sleet,
Blazing fire, and Christmas treat.

Sara Coleridge

Gillyflowers
carnations

Child's Song in Spring

The silver birch is a dainty lady,
She wears a satin gown;
The elm tree makes the old churchyard shady,
She will not live in town.

The English oak is a sturdy fellow,
He gets his green coat late;
The willow is smart in a suit of yellow
While brown the beech trees wait.

Such a gay green gown God gives the
 larches —
 As green as he is good!
 The hazels hold up their arms for arches,
 When spring rides through the wood.

 The chestnut's proud, and the lilac's pretty,
 The poplar's gentle and tall,
 But the plane tree's kind to the poor dull city —
 I love him best of all!

E Nesbit

Daffy-Down-Dilly

Daffy-Down-Dilly
Has come up to town,
In a green petticoat
And a bright yellow gown.

Anonymous

Daffy-down-dilly is
an old name for
the daffodil.

Spring, the Sweet Spring

Spring, the sweet spring, is the year's pleasant king;
Then blooms each thing, then maids dance in a ring,
Cold doth not sting, the pretty birds do sing:
Cuckoo, **jug-jug, pu-we, to-witta-woo!**

The palm and may make houses gay,
Lambs frisk and play, the shepherds pipe all day,
And we hear aye birds tune this merry lay:
Cuckoo, **jug-jug, pu-we, to-witta-woo!**

The fields breathe sweet, the daisies kiss our feet,
Young lovers meet, old wives a-sunning sit;
In every street these tunes our ears do greet:
Cuckoo, **jug-jug, pu-we, to-witta-woo!**
Spring, the sweet spring!

Thomas Nashe

Aye *always*
Lay *song*
May *hawthorn blossom*

The Man with the Beard

There was an Old Man with a beard,
Who said, "It is just as I feared! –
Two owls and a hen,
Four larks and a wren,
Have all built their nests in my beard!"

Edward Lear

There was an Old Man

There was an Old Man who said, "How
Shall I flee from that horrible cow?
I will sit on this stile,
And continue to smile,
Which may soften the heart of that cow."

Edward Lear

If you Should Meet a Crocodile

If you should meet a crocodile
Don't take a stick and poke him
Ignore the welcome in his smile,
Be careful not to stroke him.
For as he sleeps upon the Nile,
He thinner gets and thinner,
And whene'er you meet a crocodile
He's ready for his dinner.

Anonymous

The Little Cock-sparrow

A little cock-sparrow sat on a green tree,
And he chirruped, he chirruped, so merry was he;
A little cock-sparrow sat on a green tree,
And he chirruped, he chirruped, so merry was he.

A naughty boy came with his wee bow and arrow,
Determined to shoot this little cock-sparrow.
A naughty boy came with his wee bow and arrow,
Determined to shoot this little cock-sparrow.

"This little cock-sparrow shall make me a stew,
And his giblets shall make me a little pie, too."
"Oh, no!" said the sparrow, "I won't
   make a stew."
So he flapped his wings, and
   away he flew.

Anonymous

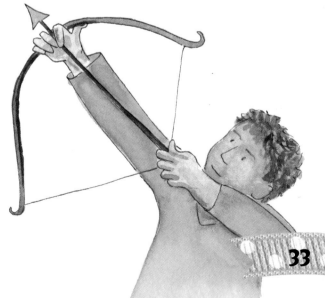

The Man who went Mad

There was a man and he went mad,
And he jumped into a biscuit bag;

The biscuit bag it was so full,
So he jumped into a roaring bull;

The roaring bull it was so fat,
So he jumped into a
gentleman's hat;

The gentleman's hat it was so fine,
So he jumped into a bottle of wine;

The bottle of wine it was so dear,
So he jumped into a barrel of beer;

The barrel of beer it was so thick,
So he jumped into a walking stick;

The walking stick it was so narrow,
So he jumped into a wheelbarrow;

The wheelbarrow began to crack,
So he jumped into a haystack;

The haystack began to blaze,
So he did nothing but cough and sneeze!

Anonymous

The Lady of Antigua

A lady there was of Antigua,
Who said to her spouse, "What a pig you are!"
He answered, "My queen
Is it manners you mean,
Or do you refer to my figure?"

G K Chesterton

The Young Lady of Norway

There was a Young Lady of Norway,
Who casually sat in a doorway;
When the door squeezed her flat,
she exclaimed "What of that?"
This courageous Young Lady
   of Norway.

Edward Lear

A Ride

A farmer went riding upon his grey mare,

Bumpety, bumpety, bump!

With his daughter behind him so rosy and fair,

Lumpety, lumpety, lump

A raven cried, "Croak!" and they all tumbled down,

Bumpety, bumpety, bump!

The mare broke her knees and the farmer his crown,

Lumpety, lumpety, lump

The mischievous raven flew laughing away,

Bumpety, bumpety, bump!

And vowed he would serve them the same the next day,

Lumpety, lumpety, lump

Anonymous

Index of First Lines

Wouldn't it be funny –   4

Amelia mixed the mustard,   6

There was a young maid who said, "Why   7

The Man in the Wilderness asked of me   8

"Sister, sister, go to bed!   10

How many seconds in a minute?   12

There was a gallant sailor-boy who'd crossed
    the harbour bar   14

Sway to and fro in the twilight grey;   16

I saw a star slide down the sky,   18

White sheep, white sheep,   19

Brown and furry   20

What is a butterfly? At best   20

Hurt no living thing: 21

The stars must make an awful noise   22

Little brown seed, oh! little brown brother;   23

January brings the snow,   24

The silver birch is a dainty lady,   26

Daffy-Down-Dilly   28

Spring, the sweet spring, is the year's pleasant king;   29

There was an Old Man with a beard,   30

There was an Old Man who said, "How   31

If you should meet a crocodile   32

A little cock-sparrow sat on a green tree,   33

There was a man and he went mad,   34

A lady there was of Antigua,   36

There was a Young Lady of Norway,   37

A farmer went riding upon his grey mare,   38